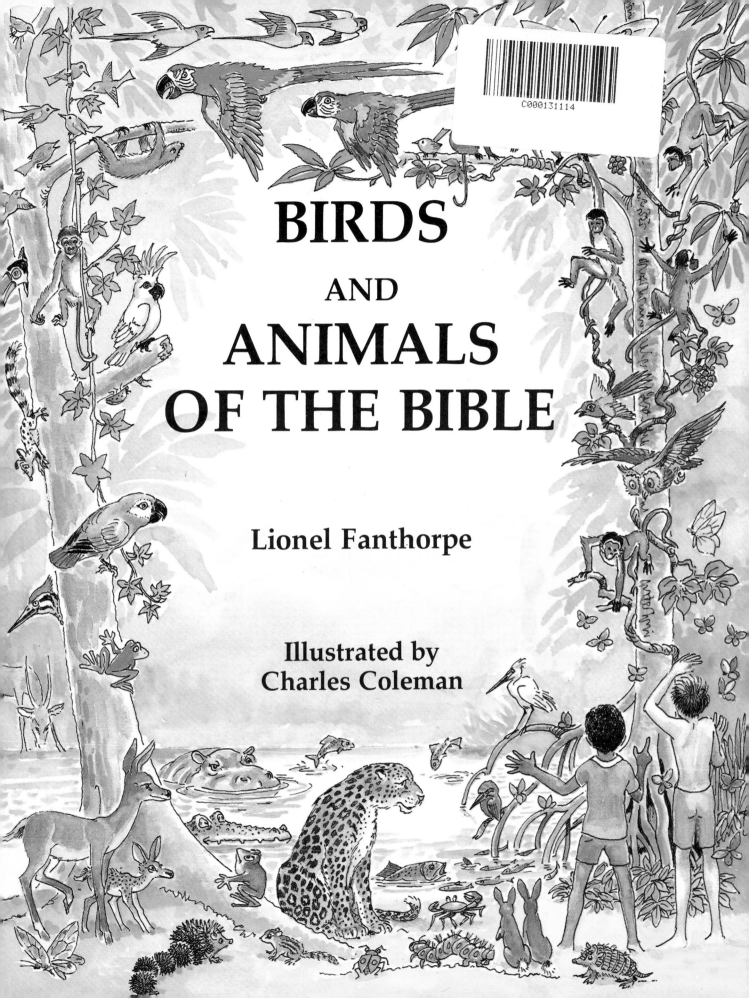

BIRDS

AND

ANIMALS

OF THE BIBLE

Lionel Fanthorpe

Illustrated by
Charles Coleman

This book is dedicated to every man, woman and child who loves birds and animals and cares for them, who feeds and protects them, and gives them sanctuary. In particular it is dedicated to the Staff of the Redwings Horse Sanctuary at Frettenham in Norfolk. May God bless and prosper your work for His creatures and repay your kindness a hundred-fold.

British Library Cataloguing in Publication Data
Fanthorpe, Lionel
  Birds & animals of the Bible.
  1. Bible
  I. Title
  220

ISBN 1-85219-0493

All enquires and requests relevant to this title should be sent to the publisher, Bishopsgate Press, 37 Union Street, London SE1 1SE

Printed in Italy by New Interlitho S.p.A. - Milan

CONTENTS

Foreword   4

Jethro's Sheep   5

Pharaoh and the Frogs   8

Balaam's Donkey   11

Jonah and the Great Fish   14

Saul and the Lost Donkeys   17

Elijah and the Ravens   20

Daniel in the Lions' Den   22

The Lost Lamb   25

The Prodigal and the Pigs   28

Lazarus and the Dogs   31

FOREWORD

CANON STANLEY MOGFORD, M.A.

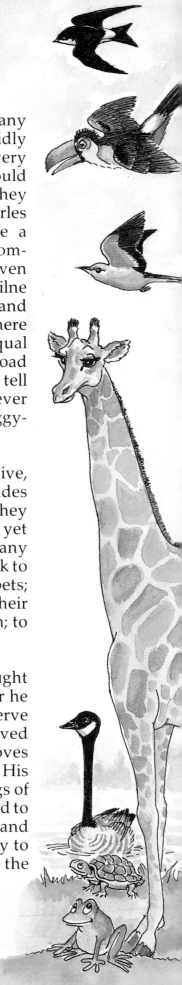

Writing for children is a gift shared by only very few. Many writers are at ease with words and can describe vividly most human situations and emotions and make a very good living from it. Even the best of them, however, would probably surrender all they have achieved if only they could equal the outstanding gifts of the Rev. Charles Dodgson, for example, who was able to overcome a strange, shy, withdrawn way of life to produce his incomparable work for children, "Alice in Wonderland". Even the most gifted of writers will continue to envy A.A. Milne with his simple, lovable stories, once told to his son, and now immortalised as "Winnie the Pooh". Why is it, where many can write and write well, there are so few to equal Kenneth Grahame with his much loved characters of Toad of Toad Hall, Badger and Mole and Ratty, or even tell stories remotely as good as Beatrix Potter's, with her never to be forgotten sketches of Squirrel Nutkin or Mrs Tiggy-winkle?

The problem will always be, even for the most creative, imaginative writers, that the world of the child eludes them. Children have such vivid imaginations that they create a world of their own that is real to them, and yet remote to the adult. Fairies are a fact of life to many children and they expect to be able to see them and talk to them. Animals are not creatures, not even merely pets; they are friends and dominate their thinking and their conversation. Magic is seen by the adult as an illusion; to the child it is real and happens.

In this book the Rev. Lionel Fanthorpe has brought together three of his great loves. He loves his Bible or he might not have been a Priest, called by its Gospel to serve his God. He loves children or he could not have survived so gallantly many years of classroom teaching. He loves animals and birds and his world is peopled with them. His prose, his poetry, his prayers, and the superb paintings of the distinguished illustrator of this book, are all directed to helping children to a love of the Bible, and of the bird and animal friends they find there. It must have been a joy to write this book; many youngsters, pray God, will have the thrill of reading it.

Stanley Mogford

Jethro's Sheep

A very long time ago, in a land called Midian, there lived a shepherd called Jethro. As well as being a shepherd, Jethro was also a priest. That meant that he helped his people to worship God, and he also helped them when they had problems and needed advice.

Jethro had no sons, but he had seven daughters, and they looked after the sheep for him while he was doing his work as a priest.

Midian was a very hot country, and there wasn't much water to be found there. This meant that the girls had to take their father's sheep to a well and draw water for them every day. Many other shepherds went to the well too, and there was often a long queue of sheep and shepherds and shepherdesses all waiting to get to the water. Some of the shepherds were rough and unkind to the girls and drove them away and stole their place in the queue. This made them late home nearly every day.

One day as they were waiting at the well, a stranger arrived. He didn't look like a shepherd. He was very big and strong, and he was dressed like an Egyptian Prince. When the shepherds tried to take the girls' turn, this stranger from Egypt told them to leave the girls alone and let them have their proper turn. Then, even though he looked like a Prince he helped them to water their sheep. That day they got home very early. Jethro was pleased and surprised. They told him about the man who had helped them.

"Go and fetch him at once!" said Jethro. "Tell him to come and have food with us." So the girls fetched him. As they shared a meal with him, he told them his name was Moses and that he had had to leave Egypt in a hurry because he had done something which had made Pharaoh, the King of Egypt, very angry. Jethro said he could stay with them, and Moses married Zipporah, Jethro's eldest daughter, and stayed in Midian with his new family for several years. One day God would call Moses to lead his own people, the Hebrews, out of slavery in Egypt, but that day was still a long way in the future.

Moses and Jethro's Sheep

Moses was a mighty man;
Very strong and brave.
He saw an Egyptian
Hurting a poor slave.

Moses got so angry —
Struck the tyrant down.
Pharaoh heard about it:
Moses left the town!

Moses fled from Egypt
Out of Pharaoh's way.
In the land of Midian
Met some girls one day.

Shepherds wouldn't give them
Water for their sheep.
Moses went to help them
For the well was deep.

Jethro was their father:
He gave Moses bread,
And his eldest daughter,
Zipporah, to wed.

Moses stayed with Jethro
For a year or two;
Till one day God gave him
Other work to do.

Prayer

Dear Lord,
Help and guide us,
As You always helped and guided
Your servant Moses.
Sometimes we find ourselves in strange places,
A new house,
A new school.
Help us to find friends in new places
As Moses found a friend in Jethro the Priest.
Help us to be like Moses
To defend the weak,
To help people who are in trouble,
To love justice,
And to fight for the right,
Wherever we are.
We ask it for the sake of Jesus Christ,
The Great Shepherd.

AMEN

Pharaoh and the Frogs

After Moses had lived with Jethro in Midian for several years he was called by God to do a very hard and dangerous job. God wanted Moses to go back to Egypt and tell Pharaoh that God wanted him to let the Israelites go. The Israelites were Hebrews, and Moses was one of them though he had been brought up as an Egyptian Prince. The Egyptians were very cruel to the Hebrews and treated them very badly. They made them work hard as slaves.

When Moses went to Pharaoh and gave him God's message, Pharaoh would not do what God said. Then all sorts of very strange and nasty things happened to the Egyptians; these strange and nasty things were called "plagues", and they went on happening until at last Pharaoh changed his mind and let the Israelites go free.

One of these plagues was that more and more *and more* frogs came along until all of Egypt seemed to be filled with them. There were frogs *everywhere.* They got into the Egyptian bakeries and into the bread. They got into all the houses and palaces. We can imagine how Pharaoh must have felt when the frogs got into *his* palace too!

The Song of the Frogs

Ribbit! Ribbit! Ribbit!
Frogs are everywhere!

Ribbit! Ribbit! Ribbit!
Sitting on each chair!

Ribbit! Ribbit! Ribbit!
Frogs are in the bread!

Ribbit! Ribbit! Ribbit!
There's one on Pharaoh's head!

Ribbit! Ribbit! Ribbit!
Frogs ten million strong!

Ribbit! Ribbit! Ribbit!
Watch us hop along!

Prayer

Dear Lord,
You made all things:
Beautiful things,
Graceful things,
Strong things
And fragile things.

You made quaint things and comical things too.

Help us to see Your work
Even in funny things like frogs,
Which make us want to laugh.

Dear Lord,
The Bible tells us
How the frogs helped
Your servant, Moses,
When He freed the Hebrew slaves
From Pharaoh in Egypt.
Help us to be useful, too, Lord,
Even though we're sometimes comical and quaint
Like the frogs.

We ask it for the sake of Jesus,
Who loves all creatures,
And every person.

AMEN

Balaam's Donkey

After Moses had led the Israelites out of Egypt, they wandered about in the wilderness for many years. At last, in God's good time, they began to conquer the Promised Land of Canaan and settle there. The people who were already living there didn't like this, and they tried to fight the Israelites to stop them coming in. One of these Kings was called Balak. He was the King of Moab, and his people were called Moabites. He sent his servants to see Balaam who was a very wise and powerful Prophet. These servants told Balaam that their master, Balak, wanted him to put a curse on the army of the Israelites, that means to say bad things about them so that they would lose the battle. Balaam said, "I am one of God's Prophets. I can only say what God tells me to say. If He wants to say bad things about the Israelites, then I can. But if He wants me to say good things, then I must say good things. I cannot say the bad things that Balak wants me to say unless God tells me to. I take my orders from God, not from King Balak." But he agreed to go with the servants and see the King all the same.

As they were on their way to see Balak, one of God's angels with a drawn sword stood in the path. He was invisible to Balaam and the other men, but Balaam's faithful donkey could see him very clearly. The donkey knew that a sword was something very dangerous, so he turned off the path and into a field. Balaam couldn't understand why his donkey had gone into the field, and he got angry and hit her. They went on a little farther and the angel with the sword blocked their way again. This time they were passing some vineyards and there were walls on each side of the path. The donkey moved sideways to avoid the angel (which Balaam couldn't see!) and she bruised Balaam's leg against the wall. Balaam got even angrier and hit her again. The angel with the sword appeared for the third time; this time there was no way round him, so the wise old donkey stood still and sank to the ground. Balaam, of course, still couldn't see the angel with the sword. He got so angry with the poor donkey that he hit her with a stick. Then a miracle happened: the donkey *spoke* to Balaam in a human voice! She explained that there was an angel with a drawn sword blocking the path. Then God opened Balaam's eyes and he saw the angel too! The angel told Balaam that the good, wise donkey which he had treated so badly had saved his life. He also told Balaam that when he saw King Balak he must be very careful to say only those things which God told him to say. Balaam said he was very sorry, and promised to do exactly what the angel told him.

Oh! Balaam, can't you see?

"Little donkey, please behave.
Today you're strange as anything!
Don't you know that Balak's waiting?
We've been sent for by the King."

"Oh, my master, can't you see him,
Standing there beside that tree?
An angel with a sword so bright:
I'll not pass! He frightens me."

"Little donkey, we're in a field!
Donkey, we've left the path behind!"
"Master, master, can't you see him?
What's the matter? Are you blind?"

"Donkey, stop! What are you doing?
Stop it now, in case I fall.
Donkey, please walk down the middle:
You've hurt my leg against this wall."

"Master, there's a shining angel!
I'm so frightened I feel weak.
Master, master, can't you see him?
How I wish that I could speak!"

Now, at last they both can see him:
Balaam got a great surprise!
For the donkey *spoke* and told him
What he'd seen with donkey's eyes.

Balaam said that he was sorry,
Knew that what he'd done was wrong;
Took his orders from the angel,
Then to Moab rode along.

Prayer

Dear Lord,
Balaam meant well,
And he was one of Your Prophets,
But he made mistakes
As we all do.
Help us never to be angry
With our friends
And those who are helping us,
Especially when we are in the wrong.
Teach us to think about things very carefully.
Make us ready to accept good advice
Even when it comes from someone
Who is younger than we are,
Or who we think doesn't know as much
As we think we know.
Make us willing to learn;
Help us to be humble.
Most of all
Help us to learn to follow Jesus,
And to keep His commandments.
We ask it for His Name's sake.

AMEN

Jonah and the Great Fish

Jonah was a Prophet, just like Balaam. He was a good man who believed in God, but, also just like Balaam, sometimes Jonah got things wrong. He didn't always do what God told him first time.

God told him to go to a big city called Nineveh and tell the people there that God was not pleased with the bad things they were doing.

Jonah did not want to go to Nineveh. He tried to run away. He got on a ship that was going the other way. There was a very big storm. The wind blew so hard that the ship nearly sank. Everyone was frightened. Jonah knew that it was his fault for not doing what he knew was right. He told the sailors that if they threw him into the sea the storm would stop. They tried hard not to do it because they did not want to hurt Jonah, but at last they agreed. As soon as Jonah had been thrown into the sea, the storm stopped and it was very calm.

God did not let Jonah come to harm: He sent a huge fish (Perhaps it was a kind of whale, but we can't be certain.) to swallow Jonah to save him from the sea. Jonah was kept alive inside this great fish for three whole days, and then the fish brought him safely to land.

God told him a second time to go to preach to the people who lived in Nineveh — and this time Jonah did as he was told! As a result of his preaching, the people all said they were sorry for what they had done wrong, and promised to live better lives in future.

Inside the Fish

The wind blew hard;
The sails were split;
The masts began to bend,
And every man on board felt sure
His life was soon to end.

"It's all my fault,"
Poor Jonah said,
"For I did not obey.
But if you throw me overboard
This wind will die away!"

The sailors were
Both brave and kind.
They did not wish him harm;
At last they had to throw him in
And then the sea grew calm.

But God had sent
A mighty fish.
It waited close at hand;
It carried Jonah safe inside
Until it reached the land.

Jonah had learnt
His lesson well:
No more he'd disobey.
When God sent him to Nineveh
He went there straight away!

So let us learn
What Jonah learnt:
God's ways are always best —
If we will trust Him and obey
Then He will do the rest!

Jonah's Prayer

Dear Lord,
I do believe in You
With all my heart,
But often I am selfish,
And often I am foolish,
Sometimes I am afraid as well.
Sometimes when I know what I should do
I don't really want to do it.
Please help me to be better.
Help me to think more about what is right,
About what You want me to do,
And please give me the strength to do it,
For Jesus' sake.

AMEN

Saul and the Lost Donkeys

Sometimes we go looking for a small copper coin and find a bar of gold instead. There was once a young man called Saul who went to look for some lost donkeys and found a crown. This is how it all happened.

Saul's father was called Kish and he had lost some donkeys. Saul was a big, strong, good-looking young man, who was much taller than most people. Kish was quite sure that his big, strong son would come to no harm if he sent him to look for the lost donkeys.

Saul had a good and wise servant with him, and after they had travelled a very long way this servant said, "There's a famous Prophet called Samuel in this city. Let's ask him to help us." Saul thought that this was a good idea, so they went to see Samuel.

Samuel not only told them that the lost donkeys had already been found, but he secretly anointed Saul (that means he poured some holy oil on his head) and told him that God had chosen him to be the first King of Israel, and that his job was to save the Israelites from their enemies, the Philistines.

Although Saul made some mistakes later on, he did some good things for his people while he was King. I expect he often remembered the time when he had gone looking for his father's lost donkeys and found the crown of Israel instead!

Saul's Lost Donkeys

A man called Kish woke up one day
And saw his donkeys were astray.

"Help me, please, " he asked his son.
"We have got to find each one."

The name of Kish's son was Saul,
And he was strong and brave and tall.

"I'll go at once, Dad," Saul replied,
And set off up the mountain side.

He took his servant, who was wise,
With loyal heart and good sharp eyes.

Behind each bush, behind each tree:
Not one donkey could they see.

They searched the caves and rocky ground:
Not one donkey could be found.

"In this city, over the fells,
A wonderful Prophet called Samuel dwells."

Saul asked the Prophet what to do.
"I've got a big surprise for you!

Your donkeys are safe: they're all back home.
There's no more need for you to roam.

But now — far more important thing —
God wants you to be the King!"

And that is how Saul — a man of renown —
Went looking for donkeys and found a crown!

Prayer When Things are Lost

Dear Lord Jesus,
You told lots of stories about lost things —
Lost money, lost animals and lost people —
Help us to find lost things.
If we lose something that is important to us
Such as a key,
Or part of a game we enjoy playing,
Help us to find it.
If we lose something important
That belongs to someone else,
Help us to find it.
If we lose our way,
If we do things that are wrong,
If we don't always keep Your Holy Laws,
Please help us to find our way back to You
And start living properly again.
If other people are lost like that,
Please help them to find themselves,
And to find You.
We ask it for Your Name's sake.

AMEN

Elijah and the Ravens

King Saul did some good things for his country, but he made lots of mistakes and did some bad things as well. A long time after Saul there was another King called Ahab who was very bad indeed — far worse than Saul. God sent a strong and brave Prophet named Elijah to put things right and to stop Ahab from doing bad things. God gave Elijah the power to stop the rain from falling, and for three years there was a drought in the land. That meant there wasn't enough water for the crops to grow properly, so food was very short, and this made it difficult for Ahab to rule the country. While the drought was on, God told Elijah to stay in hiding by a brook called Cherith near the River Jordan.

God knew that His servant Elijah needed food as well as a stream of lovely clear, fresh water to drink, so God sent ravens to feed the Prophet. A raven is a very big black bird, quite strong enough to carry pieces of food in his beak.

These ravens brought Elijah bread and meat every morning, and every evening.

20

The Song of the Raven

"I'm as black as the midnight;
Black as coal -- look at the black of my wing!
Of all the black things you have seen
Aren't I the blackest thing?

I'm as black as the pitch on a melted road;
I'm as black as chimney soot;
I'm as black as a blob of printer's ink,
Or the fur on a black cat's foot!

I can carry food in my big strong beak,
And Elijah was fed by me;
Even Jesus preached about ravens once
When He stayed in Bethany."

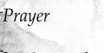

Prayer

Loving and caring Heavenly Father,
You cared for Elijah Your Prophet
During a time when there was nothing to eat.
You sent the ravens to feed him
Every morning and every night.
Jesus, Your Son our Lord,
Taught us that You care for the ravens,
And every other living thing,
Just as You cared for the Prophet Elijah.
Jesus taught us to ask for our daily bread
When He taught His disciples how to pray.
Loving Heavenly Father,
Give us our daily bread,
And everything else we need
Because You know our needs better than we do.
We ask it in Jesus' Name.

AMEN

Daniel in the Lions' Den

Because some of their kings, like Ahab, had been very bad, and some of their kings, like Saul, had made big mistakes, the Jewish nation was beaten in war by the Babylonians, and many of the Jews were taken away as prisoners to Babylon. They were in exile there for many years. Exile means being away from home when you don't want to be, and nobody likes being away from parents, brothers and sisters, families and friends. Home with a loving family is the best place in the whole world.

One of the Jews living in Babylon during this long exile was called Daniel. He was very brave, very clever and most important of all he was very good. He loved God with all his heart, and always tried hard to do what God wanted.

Because Daniel was a good, clever and honest man, King Darius had made him one of the chief rulers of Babylon, and this made a lot of bad men very jealous. They plotted against Daniel, and tried hard to get him into trouble. One day these enemies told the King that he should pass a law saying that everybody had to ask him if they wanted anything. They mustn't ask anyone else, and they mustn't pray to God for anything.

Of course, they knew that Daniel would have to break this law, because he always asked God for things and prayed to God every day. This new law also said that if anyone broke it, he would be put into a den of lions.

The King was very sorry that Daniel's enemies had played this cunning trick on him, but once the law had been made it had to be kept, so Daniel was lowered into the lions' den and the top was sealed with a big stone. All that night King Darius could not sleep because he was so worried about his friend Daniel. First thing in the morning he went to the den and called out to see if Daniel was still alive.

"No harm has come to me," answered Daniel, "because God has sent one of His angels to protect me from the lions." So the King gave orders that Daniel was to be let out at once. All the bad and jealous men who had tricked the King and had had Daniel put in the lions' den were put into it themselves — and they didn't get out!

Daniel and Darius

In the ages long, long gone
Darius ruled in Babylon.
Daniel was the King's best friend,
One he trusted to the end.

Jealous enemies he had —
Always plotting something bad!
Passed a law which said that men
Who prayed must face the lions' den!

Into the den brave Daniel went:
A sleepless night King Darius spent:
In the morning safe and sound —
With the lions underground.

God had sent an angel bright:
He kept Daniel safe all night.
In his anger Darius said:
"The plotters now go in instead!"

The men who wanted Daniel dead
To the hungry lions were fed!
You should never plot to do
What you'd not like done to you!

23

Pray as Daniel Prayed

Almighty and ever loving Father,
Help us to pray just as Daniel prayed.
When we are in danger, please protect us.
When we are in difficulty, show us the way through it
When we are happy, help us to share it with You,
And with other people.
When we are sad, please comfort us.
When we are angry without a cause,
Make us calm and peaceful again.
When everything is fine,
And life is going well,
Help us to pray, not because we need anything,
Not because we want anything,
But simply because we love You,
And enjoy talking to You in prayer.
Help us to listen, as well, dear Lord,
And to remember that listening is even more important
Than talking.
We ask it for the sake of Jesus,
Whose prayers were always perfect,
And who taught the disciples how to pray.

AMEN

24

The Lost Lamb

This is a story that Jesus Himself told to teach people how much God loves each one of us, and how important it is to God that we should all be happy with Him forever. Jesus lived in a place and at a time when looking after sheep was one of the jobs that many people did. Because there were so many sheep and shepherds in Palestine then, Jesus knew that everybody would understand a story about a lost lamb; most people would have seen lost sheep and heard them bleating while they tried to find their way back to the rest of the flock.

No doubt Jesus had many shepherds among His friends and followers, and perhaps He heard one of them talking about a lost lamb which he had found again and how happy he was when he had found it.

Once upon a time there was a shepherd who had 100 sheep. He was a very good and caring shepherd, and he loved every one of his flock. He knew them so well that he had a name for each one, and he used to call them by name when he led them to good, fresh, green pastures.

Then one lamb wandered away and got lost. The shepherd counted his flock twice that night, and he counted very slowly and carefully so that he did not make any mistakes: there were only ninety-nine safely in the fold — one baby lamb was missing! Although it was dangerous to go out alone at night because of hungry wild animals and robbers, the brave and loving shepherd set off at once to find the lost lamb.

He travelled miles and miles over rough and dangerous country, often he hurt himself on sharp rocks and thorns in the dark, but he kept steadily on his way. He had made up his mind not to give up looking until he found his lost lamb.

At last he saw her, lonely and very frightened, tired out and hopelessly lost. With a great shout of joy, he picked the little lost lamb up in his strong arms and carried her all the way back to the sheep fold. Then, very gently, he got her some food and put her back safely with the others. Now when he counted them again he had the 100 he knew he should have had in the first place.

The shepherd was happy. The sheep were happy. The little lost lamb was the happiest sheep of all!

The Song of the Lost Lamb

It seemed such fun when I began;
I thought I'd slip away.
The grass looked greener over there.
It was a lovely day.

The sun was warm upon my wool;
The grass was very sweet;
The pasture sloped so gently down
Beneath my skipping feet.

But bit by bit the sky grew dark.
The wind began to blow.
The grass had turned to cold hard rocks,
And it began to snow.

I heard the howling of the wolf;
The growling of the bear;
The roaring of the hungry lion —
My heart was filled with fear.

I wondered where my shepherd was,
My father and my mother:
I wished that I was safely home
And warm beside my brother!

Lonely and lost in that wild place;
I bleated and I cried.
Unless my shepherd had appeared,
I'm sure I would have died.

It was so lovely when he came,
His arms around me strong.
I think I must have gone to sleep
As he carried me along.

Next thing I knew I was safe home
With all the other sheep;
I am so happy to be back —
Now close to him I'll keep!

The Lost Lamb's Prayer

Loving and Eternal Shepherd,
Thank You for being so good to us;
Especially when we are silly and go away from You.
Thank You for bringing us safely back again.
Help us to learn the true meaning of life,
And to stay close to You at all times.
Help us to help You to find the other lost lambs.
May the things we do and the things we say
Show people around us that we belong to You,
And when they can see a little of You in us
In spite of our many faults and weaknesses,
May that help them to find You for themselves
Loving, caring Shepherd of us all,
Bless and help all Your poor lost and frightened ones,
And bring them safely to the Eternal Home,
Where, one day, we shall be happy with You forever.

AMEN

The Prodigal and the Pigs

This is another of the stories which Jesus told to teach people about the love and mercy of God the Father, and how happy He is to welcome us back when we say we are sorry and come home to Him again. In this story it was not a lamb that was lost, but a young man. He is called 'prodigal' because he spent his money without thinking, and that is what prodigal means — it is almost the same as 'spendthrift'.

This young man asked his father if he could have straight away the share of the money which would one day come to him when his father died. His father was a good and generous man, and gave his son what he asked for. The young prodigal went on a wild spending spree. He bought lots of food and drink for his many new 'friends' who were not friends at all but only stayed with him for the sake of what he bought for them. At last all his money had gone, and he was hungry. All his new 'friends' had disappeared as soon as his money had run out! Not one of them would help him. He found a very poorly paid job working for a man who kept pigs. These pigs were well-fed and happy; they had more to eat than the boy had! He was so hungry that he even tried some of their food, but although it tasted nice to the pigs and did them good, it was not good for human beings!

Then the prodigal started to think; he thought how well his father treated the servants back home; they were well fed and well dressed and they had warm, clean, comfortable beds to sleep in. "I'll go back home," he said to himself. "I'll tell father how stupid I've been and how truly sorry I am now; then I'll ask him to take me on just as a servant. I don't deserve to be a son again." He set off for home at once.

His father loved him very much and had been looking out for him ever since he had left. As soon as his father saw him in the distance he ran to meet him and made him very, very welcome. He held a special feast that night to show how happy he was to have him back.

In a way, it was the pigs that he was caring for which helped the prodigal to see the truth: when he realised that even they were better fed than he was, he knew that the only sensible thing to do was to go home.

The Prodigal's Poem

I left my home with a heart so high:
There was golden sun and a bright blue sky.
My clothes were new and my purse was full;
And I felt as strong as a Bashan bull!
I was young and free and the world was mine —
And I never thought about feeding swine!

I made new friends and I made them fast:
I thought that my money would always last.
I would buy them drinks, and this and that —
Until one day my purse went flat.
There was no more singing, or dancing jigs —
But I still never thought about feeding pigs!

Not one of them gave me a helping hand;
Then a terrible famine attacked that land.
Hungry and thin, I began to sob;
Then a kind old farmer gave me a job.
The pay was low, and the job was hard —
I fed the pigs in the farmer's yard!

I thought of the home I'd left behind,
And although the farmer was fairly kind,
I still hadn't got enough to eat:
What's good for a pig is not man's meat!
I swallowed my pride and I set off home;
I'd had my lesson — no more I'd roam.

I wondered what my Dad would say,
But he ran to meet me on the way.
My Father embraced me and called me son,
And a happy new life has just begun.
A farmer learns from the soil he digs —
But I learnt my lesson from feeding pigs!

A Prayer for Prodigals

Loving heavenly Father,
We thank You for all the wonderful truths
That Your Son, Jesus, taught us.
We thank You for the story of the Prodigal Son,
And for what it teaches us
About Your love and mercy.
Dear Father, we are much too often like that boy.
We leave You without any good reason.
We disobey.
We break Your Holy Laws
Which are there to guide and protect us.
Help us to come to our senses,
Like he did.
Help us to see that the only place where we can be happy
Is with You.
Help us to be truly sorry for our sins,
Like he was.
Welcome us as his father welcomed him.
For the sake of Jesus, our Lord,
Who taught us about Your Love and Mercy.

AMEN

Lazarus and the Dogs

This is another of the wonderful stories which Jesus told. Once upon a time there was a poor, sick, old beggar named Lazarus. He lived in the street outside the grand house of a very rich man called Dives. He used to beg for the scraps of food that fell from the rich man's table. Nobody bothered with the poor, ill, old man except some stray dogs: they were lost and unwanted just like he was, but they used to come and lick him in the way that some dogs do when they want to make friends. It would be nice to think that poor Lazarus got some comfort from the dogs, and felt that they wanted him even if no-one else did. At last he died, and was taken by the angels straight up to Heaven, where he enjoyed wonderful happiness with God. When the rich man, Dives, died, he didn't go to Heaven, but was very, very unhappy. If only he had really cared for Lazarus while they both lived on earth, and used some of his great wealth to help the poor, things would have been very different, and he and Lazarus could have gone to Heaven together.

The Song of Lazarus

"I lay outside the rich man's gate, and begged when I was
  able,
But Dives only sent me scraps that fell from off his table!
The poor, stray dogs were my only friends.
I wonder what happens when this life ends?"

The angels answered Lazarus with endless joy above,
But Dives learnt that rich men ought to treat the poor with
  love.

Prayer for the Poor

Dear Lord,
You own everything: all the gold and silver;
All the diamonds and emeralds and rubies.
What we think of as our money is only on loan from You
While we're here on earth.
Teach us to be good stewards of Your money,
And to give the poor what they need.
We ask it in the Name of Jesus,
Who gave up all the riches of Heaven, and became poor
For our sakes.

AMEN